Herbal Remedies for Dogs and Cats
A Pocket Guide to Selection and Use

Mary Wulff-Tilford and Gregory L. Tilford

Mountain Weed Publishing ● **Conner, Montana**

About the Authors

Mary Wulff-Tilford is a professional member of the American Herbalist's Guild who devotes her time and expertise to the holistic care of animals. She is founder of a company which produces low-alcohol herb extracts for dogs and cats, and is respected by holistic veterinarians and pet owners worldwide as a leading holistic pet care consultant and teacher.

Gregory L. Tilford is co-owner and formulating herbalist of a company which produces glycerin-based herb extracts for dogs and cats. He is a contributing editor and herb advisor for *Natural Pet* magazine (Fancy Publications), and is the founding president of the Natural Pet Products Association. Greg is author of two books on wild medicinal plants: *The EcoHerbalist's Fieldbook* (Mountain Weed Publishing, 1993), and *Edible & Medicinal Plants of the West* (Mountain Press Publishing, 1997).

Mary and Gregory are currently completing a comprehensive, fully-illustrated guide book on herbs for animals.

HERBAL REMEDIES FOR DOGS AND CATS
A Pocket Guide to Selection and Use

Copyright ©1997 Mary Wulff-Tilford and Gregory L. Tilford

All Rights Reserved

No part of this book may be reproduced in any form without the expressed permission of the publisher.

ISBN: 0-9638638-8-6

Printed in the United States of America
by Professional Impressions, Darby, MT.

Mountain Weed Publishing
P.O. Box 212, 155 Conner Cutoff Rd.
Conner, MT 59827

♻ *Text Printed on Recycled Paper*

Using Herbs Naturally

Old ways die hard — especially if we have been raised with them. In our society, mainstream approaches to health maintenance focus on symptomatic intervention with disease. Typically, when a person or animal gets sick, the conventional practitioner works to identify and suppress uncomfortable or unsightly symptoms in order to achieve immediate results. As children, most of us are taught time and again to confront fever with aspirin — dandruff with shampoos — constipation with laxatives.

But what about the *causes* of these discomforts? Are we really taking a curative approach toward a fever without recognizing its origin and its purpose? *Why* do we have dandruff anyway? *Why* are our animals suffering chronic constipation? These are questions that are addressed by the holistic herbalist; one who looks at the body as an entire, intricately- balanced biocommunity of countless organs, chemicals, micro-organisms and life energies. From a holistic perspective, the herbalist realizes that all body functions are interdependent— and that physical or emotional discomforts do not represent the totality of a health crisis. Instead, he or she recognizes symptoms as the body's way of conveying an underlying imbalance; a state of "dis-ease". Still, it's hard for any of us to step away from such strong predisposition, as evidenced by millions of people who search out natural alternatives only to treat dandruff with herbal shampoos, or arthritis with herbs that confront discomfort, but not cause— such as yucca or licorice. Many of these people find that the natural products they are using do not yield the quick-fix results they are used to, and they quickly become discouraged. Eventually these people abandon herbs, homeopathy, supplements, and flower essences in favor of their old "brand-x". Is it because natural medicines don't work? certainly not! The problems that lead to frustration in many herb consumers stem not from the quality or effectiveness of the products they are employing, but from the principles by which they are used.

Many herbs will work quite well at bringing about symptomatic relief. After all, about 80% of modern mainstream medicine has been conceived from a botanical origin. But, when herbs are used in an allopathic capacity, their greatest healing gifts are not employed. When using herbs, a curative approach is incomplete in absence of holistic perspective, and in the aforementioned examples, yucca and licorice are being used as nothing more than just another over-the-counter, band-aid remedy.

The key to accessing the full potential of herbal medicine rests in how well we can embrace a holistic perspective of the natural healing process. For most of us this means putting old predispositions aside, revving up some imagination, and engaging in some open-minded observation. We don't need bioscience degrees to embrace the principles of effective herbalism, but we must learn to identify good health, and we must learn to recognize subtle changes in the subject we are treating.

In holistic medicine, "good health" is viewed as the maintenance of proper balance within a complex, finely tuned system. All elements of the mind, body, and spirit must be maintained at optimum levels of cooperative efficiency if the healing process is to occur, and we must realize that if any element of the collective whole fails at its job, an imbalance (dis-ease) will result. To accomplish this, a proactive approach toward health and well-being is an absolute necessity, and proper diet is needed as the foundation from which to base our holistic efforts of assisting the body at what it is designed to do best: *heal itself.*

The Herb-Diet Connection

The body requires fuel and building materials in order to function as Nature designed it, and proper, natural function is exactly what the herbalist wishes to maintain. Herbs help to bridge the gap between what the body needs to function properly from diet and exercise, and what it needs to receive from time to time, in extra support of natural body functions. In nature, wild animals have an instinctive ability to use herbs in a manner that allows them to receive the nutrition and specialized support their bodies need. Even domesticated animals retain part of this ability — dogs eat grass; my cat nibbles aloe on occasion (although she obviously dislikes it). But in domestication, animals have neither the botanical diversity, or enough intact instinct to selectively choose the herbs they need. Instead they must rely on us.

Herbs work to support body functions in circumstances where proper nutrition alone cannot regain or maintain a state of balance. With this in mind, it is very important to realize that herbs cannot replace the body's requirement of good diet; that the medicinal activities of herbs in the body work in *concert* with the quality of food that goes into it. Without quality nutrition, herbs are holistically useless in therapeutic applications.

Just like us, animals need raw, unprocessed foods that are rich in a diversity of live enzymes and nutrients. Learn to feed your animals a natural diet, supplemented if necessary with a good quality commercial food. Good nutrition is the first step in achieving a state of healthy balance... without it, the body is already dis-eased.

Herb Actions and Special Affinities

It is unrealistic to think a full conveyance of effective herbal wisdom can be contained in this booklet, but a large measure of awareness can be perpetuated by embracing a basic understanding of how each plant works within the body. In Western herbalism, the effects that plant materials have in or on the body are called "medicinal actions" or "active properties". By becoming familiar with the medicinal actions of the herbs you have access to, you will have a good idea where to look for an appropriate course of therapy when a need arises. In addition to the manner by which herbs work in the body, it is also important to begin learning each herb's specialty, or *systemic affinity*; its special kinship with certain portions of the anatomy. For instance, we may know that slippery elm has a general *astringent action* (meaning that it shrinks tissues), but its effective usefulness is really pronounced when we know that it has a special *affinity* to the digestive tract—where its astringent actions are particularly well suited to shrinking the inner wall of the small intestine to relieve diarrhea and other discomforts.

Dosages and Duration

Dosage and duration of an herb therapy is relative to the specific needs, tolerances, and metabolism of the animal receiving the herb. In other words, the answers to how much and for how long may vary from animal to animal. The key to successful healing with herbs rests in how well you know your animal, and how accurately you note its responses to specific herbal remedies. A conservative starting point for administration of herb extracts, infusions, or dried herbs in dogs, cats, and herbivores is to use only one or two herbs at a time, and to proportion the animal's body weight to the recommended human dosage; based on your veterinarian's opinion, a reputable reference book, or the product manufacturer's recommendations. For example, a thirty pound dog would receive one fifth of that which is recommended for a 150 pound human.

Remember: this is a starting point— dogs, cats, and other carnivores have much faster metabolic rates than we do, and therefore, dosage might have to be increased later to achieve the results you are looking for. Whith most herbs, this is safely accomplished by increasing the dose in 10 percent increments, if needed, to a maximum of seventy five percent above the starting dose. In other words, if you have determined that the starting dose for *Max* is twenty drops of burdock extract, twice daily, then you can increase the dose two drops at a time; until you reach thirty-five drops, if necessary. Most animals will require a dose two to three times daily.

Duration of an herbal therapy also depends on the specific animal, and will also vary according to the dis-ease you are confronting. Generally, it is best to take at least a two day break from herbal therapies each week (five days on, two days off). This allows you to monitor the body's responses to the herbs, and to alleviate any tolerance or toxicity problems the animal may otherwise develop as a result of long-term use. The duration required to see results varies greatly, and is dependent on the nature of the herb, the animal, and the severity of the imbalance you are confronting. If results don't begin to materialize after you have maintained a maximum dosage schedule for more than ten days, it may be time to try another herb, or to consult your holistic veterinarian. In any case, keep good records of your successes, failures, and observations. Exactly how long to maintain an herbal therapy can only be determined through experience and familiarity with your animal, and good record keeping is instrumental to becoming an effective herbalist.

Types of Herbal Preparations

The manner in which an herb is used is determined by a holistic assessment of the circumstances at hand, and the overall nature of the subject animal. Once we have investigated the origins of the symptoms that have caught our attention, we can select the medicinal actions we need to confront the problem. This will lead us to several herb choices, from which we can choose one or more that have a specific affinity to the body systems that are involved. From this, we must choose an herbal preparation that fits the circumstances.

Dried, Bulk Herb Material

Dried bulk herbs are handy to have around, as they allow a great deal of diversity in how they can be prepared and applied. In addition to use in various herb preparations, some dried herbs can be sprinkled directly onto your pet's food. As a general rule, roots will keep two to three times longer than dried leaf material, but don't stock-up on more than you can use within one year, and be sure to store your herbs in airtight containers that are kept away from sunlight. Regardless of proper storage methods, dried herbs will eventually oxidize and loose their potency. A few herbs loose much of their medicinal, nutritive value within days of drying. Buy from an honest, knowledgeable herbalist who knows the origin of his or her merchandise, or grow your own to assure optimum potency and shelf life.

Fresh Herbs

Fresh herbs, clipped, dug, or plucked directly from the garden are rich in nutrients and medicinal constituents. Provided that their physical nature allows for the form of preparation you need, fresh herbs are without compare in terms of medicinal potency. Some herbs however, are very strong when used fresh, while others require at least partial drying before they will impart their active constituents into a useful medium. Cascara sagrada bark is one example— this herbal laxative is far too strong if used fresh, and should be dried for at least a full year to "mellow" it before use. It is also poorly water soluble when fresh, and until it dries it will not infuse adequately in water for a good tea.

Herb Capsules

Because of their short, fast digestive tracts, encapsulated herbs tend to pass right through dogs and cats. Even if they don't, you may find some difficulty in getting a large enough dose into your animal. In horses, sheep, llamas, goats, and other herbivores, capsules work fine— but plan on feeding dozens of them. In these animals, you are often better off feeding the bulk herb, or using an extract.

Alcohol Extracts, or "Tinctures"

With very few exceptions, an alcohol tincture is by far the most versatile, strongest, and readily usable form of herb preparation. Using specific formulas to match each herb, a tincture is prepared by soaking a measured quantity of fresh or dried herb in a certain proportion of alcohol and water. The alcohol serves as a solvent which breaks down the plant material and releases the active constituents into a liquid base, called a "menstruum". After two days to two weeks (depending on the method of process) the menstruum is then strained from the plant material (called the "marc"), to produce the finished, liquid product. Alcohol tinctures offer the advantages of maximum potency and unlimited shelf life (provided they are stored properly). The concentrated, liquid nature of tincture preparations allows for quick and complete absorption into the body, even in the short digestive tracts of dogs and cats. The problem with these preparations is getting it into the animal — alcohol extracts are typically 30-70% grain alcohol, and while typical dosages do not present any alcohol-toxicity problems, animals truly hate the taste of them. Alcohol tinctures can also be used in topical applications, and can be carefully diluted into water or as a part of an eye, hair, or skin rinse.

Glycerin-based Herb Extracts (or "Glycerites")

Glycerites are made by essentially the same methods as an alcohol extract, but vegetable glycerin is used in place of alcohol. The big advantage of glycerites in animal care is their palatability— glycerin tastes very sweet, with a flavor and consistency that is similar to light corn syrup. While some glycerin-based extracts are not as potent as their alcohol counterparts, they allow the pet owner to get the herb into their animal in the first place—hence, half the battle is then won. Potency issues can then be adjusted by increasing the dosage. Glycerites will not keep indefinitely, but will remain viable for at least two years if refrigerated. Vegetable glycerin is refined from coconut oils, and despite its syrupy-sweet flavor, it is metabolized in a manner similar to a triglyceride; not a sugar. This means it can be used safely in animals with alcohol sensitivity or in those with diabetes.

Water Infusions (herb teas)

Infusions are made by steeping a specific quantity of plant material in hot water. The

disadvantages of using teas internally for animals should be obvious... most animals don't like tea. However, palates vary from critter to critter, and sometimes they will drink it up. Infusions are especially useful for skin and coat rinses.

Decoctions

A decoction is an infusion that requires some gentle simmering to make a strong enough preparation for therapeutic use. This is required of many roots; when the plant material is too insoluble in water to allow a strong enough infusion. Decoctions should be prepared using a minimum of heat— simmer the herb for about 15 minutes, at a temperature that is only slightly boiling. Too much heat will destroy many of the plant constituents you wish to employ. Decoctions are used in the same manner as water infusions, but they tend to be very strong in comparison.

Oil Infusions

An oil infusion is produced by completely covering an herb with olive oil and allowing it to steep in a covered, non-metallic container, in warm location, for at least one month. The oil is then pressed out and stored in the refrigerator for up to one year. Although several choices of oil can be used, olive oil possesses its own preservative qualities, is relatively affordable, and is nourishing to the body; both internally and externally. Oil infusions are excellent for topical applications, acting to soothe and protect the affected area while acting to hold herb constituents at the site where they are applied.

Poultices

A poultice is made by mashing plant material (usually dried foliage) with enough water or vegetable oil to make a wet, pesto-like paste. Poultices are very good in topical field applications, when other preparations are impossible.

Salves and Ointments

Salves and ointments are simply thickened oil infusions. To make a salve, beeswax is often used as the thickening agent, whereas the thinner ointment preparations typically employ coconut butter — particularly if they are to be used in suppository applications. The oil infusion is gently heated, and the beeswax or coconut butter is melted into the liquid until the cooled product yields the desired consistency.

Fomentations

A fomentation is used for topical applications; where a water or oil infusion must remain on a specific body site for a specific period. Gauze or other cloth material is placed over the subject area, and the infusion is poured onto the dressing until it is soaked. Mustard packs, castor oil packs, and other traditional remedies employ this method. This is a good approach for horses with fungal infections of the skin, or other animals who don't mind "wearing" an herbal ornament for awhile.

A List of Herbs A to Z

Before using any form of plant medicine, it's good common sense to first find out if your animal is allergic to it. Rub a small quantity of whatever preparation onto your pet's skin, and watch for reddening, itching, or any other warning signs *before* continuing intended use. Then... use just a small first dose, and watch for results again. To determine a starting dosage, read pages 2-3.

Alfalfa - *Medicago sativa*
Parts Used: leaves, stems, unopened flowers
Actions: nutritive, anti-inflammatory, diuretic
Affinities: muscloskeletal system
Specific Uses: shown to help reduce rheumatic pain when used over a long term; increases appetite
Availability: health food stores, can be propagated in the garden
Preparation: bulk herb, capsules, infusion, or extract
Alternative herbs: dandelion, red clover
Cautions and Comments: contains saponins; may cause nausea in some animals if used in large quantities over extended periods. Seeds may be toxic.

Aloe vera - *Aloe species*
Parts Used: juice
Actions: soothes and protects (internally and externally), speeds healing of injuries, anti-tumor
Affinities: skin and digestive tract
Specific Uses: injuries and irritations of the skin, digestive tract, urinary system. Laxative.
Availability: easy to grow; widely available in the market place
Preparation: fresh, pressed juice
Alternative Herbs: chickweed, marshmallow, cleavers, plantain (psyllium), calendula
Cautions & Comments: use *only* the juice of this plant. The skin may cause severe digestive upset and uncontrollable diarrhea.

Bee Balm - *Monarda species*
Parts Used: flowers and foliage
Actions: expels gas, antibacterial, astringent, diuretic
Affinities: digestive and urinary tracts
Specific Uses: acute gastritis, or use in place of sage as an antibacterial. Especially useful for gum inflammations and to fight gingivitis.
Availability: some herb stores, nurseries, widely distributed in the wild
Preparation: infusion, extract, poultice
Alternative Herbs: sage
Cautions & Comments: safe for long term, but suspect the presence of herbicides if you gather this plant from the wild.

Black Walnut - *Juglans nigra*

Parts Used: green, unripe hulls
Actions: expels intestinal parasites, astringent
Affinities: digestive tract
Specific Uses: tapeworms, symptomatic control of diarrhea
Availability: extract is available at herb stores
Preparation: extract
Alternative Herbs: garlic, oregon grape, pumpkin seeds, sage
Cautions & Comments: combines well with garlic and pumpkin seeds for use against tapeworms. May cause digestive disorders if used over an extended period.

Bugleweed - *Lycopus americanus*

Parts Used: all above-ground parts
Actions: analgesic, sedative, hypothyroid
Affinities: thyroid, nervous system
Specific Uses: may be useful in animals with hyperthyroid conditions.
Availability: herb stores; widely distributed in the wild.
Preparation: extract
Alternative Herbs: feverfew (for pain)
Cautions & Comments: do not use in animals with depressed thyroid function. Use only as directed by a trained practitioner.

Burdock - *Arctium lappa*

Parts Used: Root
Actions: blood cleansing, liver stimulating, nutritive
Affinities: liver, especially when associated with dermatitis or dandruff
Specific Uses: eczema, allergies, systemic toxicity
Availability: health food stores; seed available from catalogs
Preparation: extract, infusion, bulk fresh herb.
Alternative Herbs: dandelion, red clover, chicory
Cautions and Comments: combines well with dandelion, red clover, or alfalfa for chronic skin conditions. Safe in long term use. Beware of herbicides on wild plants.

Calendula - *C. officinalis*

Parts Used: flowers
Actions: anti-inflammatory, astringent, speeds healing, soothing to skin and mucous membranes
Affinities: skin and digestive tract
Specific Uses: topically or internally for wounds, inflammations, and irritations; stomach upset
Availability: herb stores
Preparation: water or oil infusion, extract
Alternative Herbs: aloe vera, comfrey, chamomile
Cautions & Comments: combines well with St. John's Wort, garlic oil, mullein, or oregon grape for topical use on injuries.

Catnip - *Nepeta cataria*
Parts Used: all aboveground parts
Actions: carminative, anti-spasmodic, mild sedative
Affinities: digestive tract and nervous system
Specific Uses: stomach upset; relaxing and sedative tea
Availability: health food stores; seed available from catalogs
Preparation: extract or infusion
Alternative herbs: chamomile, bee balm, valerian, skullcap
Cautions and Comments: the leaves are safe, however the seeds may be toxic.

Cats' Claw - *Uncaria tomentosa*
Parts Used: root and vine inner bark
Actions: boosts autoimmune functions; anti-inflammatory; speeds healing; antitumor
Affinities: autoimmune system
Specific Uses: systemic support at the onset of bacterial, viral, or fungal infections
Availability: wild-harvested from Peruvian rain forests. Widely available in the market.
Preparation: extract, infusion, encapsulated herb.
Alternative Herbs: echinacea, astragalus
Cautions & Comments: the hot "buzz" in the current herb market. Concerns of over-harvest and rain forest defoliation are continuing to grow.

Cayenne - *Capsicum annum and frutescens*
Parts Used: dried seed pods
Actions: dilates blood vessels, stops bleeding, vascular tonic, respiratory stimulant
Affinities: digestive, respiratory, and circulatory systems
Specific Uses: circulatory deficiencies, pulmonary edema, slows external and internal bleeding.
Availability: at the supermarket or herb store.
Preparation: encapsulated or bulk powder.
Alternative Herbs: ginger, shepherd's purse, or any variety of mustard seed
Cautions & Comments: may cause instantaneous blistering. A good choice for chronic or acute respiratory or digestive tract bleeding. Avoid contact with the eyes.

Chamomile - *Matricaria chamomile*
Parts Used: flowering tops
Actions: sedative, anti-spasmodic, digestive, anti-inflammatory
Affinities: nervous, digestive, urinary, musculo-skeletal, skin
Specific Uses: asthma, allergies, bronchitis, stomachache, gingivitis, eye wash (conjunctivitis)
Availability: health food stores; seed available from catalogs
Preparation: infusion
Alternative herbs: rosemary, catnip, bee balm, skullcap, valerian
Cautions and Comments: those allergic to ragweed should avoid chamomile, otherwise it is very safe. A good choice for long term applications.

Chaparral (creosote bush) - *Larrea tridentata*

Parts Used: leaf and stem
Actions: antiseptic
Affinities: skin
Specific Uses: skin wash for flea bites and acute dermatitis
Availability: herb stores; abundant in the desert southwest
Preparation: decoction
Alternative Herbs: chamomile, sage, juniper
Cautions & Comments: although an excellent liver herb stimulant, this plant may cause liver damage if used improperly. The FDA has labeled this herb as unsafe for internal use.

Chickweed - *Stellaria media*

Parts Used: all aboveground parts
Actions: demulcent, emollient, lymphatic tonic
Affinities: digestive tract; lymph system
Specific Uses: soothing to the digestive tract, lymphatic blockages, soothing to the skin
Availability: easily grown as a garden weed
Preparation: fresh plant tea or extract
Alternative herbs: cleavers, aloe, marshmallow
Cautions and Comments: may have laxative effects if consumed in large quantities.

Cleavers - *Gallium aparine*

Parts Used: aboveground parts
Actions: diuretic, alterative, anti-inflammatory, tonic, astringent
Affinities: lymphatic, spleen, kidneys
Specific Uses: anti-inflammatory and antispasmodic on urinary muscle wall
Availability: herb stores/health food stores
Preparation: fresh juice or fresh plant extract
Alternative herbs: Gallium boreale
Cautions and Comments: also useful for fibroid tumors and chronic cysts.

Coltsfoot - *Petasites spp.*

Parts Used: leaves and flowers
Actions: anti-spasmodic and expectorant with anti-inflammatory properties
Affinities: lungs
Specific Uses: coughs, bronchitis, silicosis
Availability: herb stores
Preparation: extract or tea
Alternative herbs: mullein, goldenrod, grindelia, comfrey
Cautions and Comments: may contain potentially carcinogenic alkaloid constituents. Do not use for periods of more than 10 days

Comfrey - *Symphytum officinale*

Parts Used: leaf
Actions: soothing and protecting to tissues; speeds healing, internally and externally.

Affinities: skin and digestive tract

Specific Uses: an excellent primary ingredient in healing salves, ointments, and topically-applied oil infusions

Availability: herb stores; easy to grow from nursery stock

Preparation: infusion (oil or water), salves, bulk dry or fresh herb as a feed supplement

Alternative Herbs: calendula, chamomile, St. John's wort

Cautions & Comments: because it contains potentially carcinogenic alkaloids, comfrey is regarded as "unsafe for internal use" by the FDA. For open wounds, combine with an antibacterial, such as oregon grape.

Cornsilk - *Zea mays*

Parts Used: the fresh (not dried), soft threads (stigma) from the female flowers

Actions: diuretic, tonic, and soothing to membranes

Affinities: genito-urinary and kidneys

Specific Uses: acute urinary inflammations, stones; chronic kidney problems

Availability: organic food stores; clipped from organically-grown ears of corn

Preparation: infusion, extract, encapsulated, bulk

Alternative Herbs: marshmallow, chickweed, plantain

Cautions & Comments: combines well with couchgrass and echinacea for urinary inflammations and infections; including FUS. Safe for long term use. Herbivores enjoy eating this herb.

Couchgrass - *Agropyron repens*

Parts Used: rhizomes(rootlets)

Actions: demulcent, tonic, diuretic, antimicrobial, anti-inflammatory

Affinities: genito-urinary system

Specific Uses: urethritis, cystitis, kidney or bladder stones, FUS

Availability: common garden grass weed; also known as "quackgrass" or "dog grass"

Preparation: infusion, extract, or fresh green leaves as part of diet

Alternative herbs: parsley seed, dandelion leaf, horsetail

Cautions and Comments: always suspect the presence of herbicide on this weed. Combines very well with echinacea, cornsilk, horsetail, and dandelion for inflammatory urinary problems.

Dandelion - *Taraxacum officinalis*

Parts Used: roots and leaves

Actions: leaves are diuretic, and roots for liver conditions, anti-rheumatic

Affinities: urinary system; liver

Specific Uses: leaves as a strong diuretic, roots for liver problems and rheumatoid conditions. Flowers are high in lecithin.

Availability: common garden weed

Preparation: leaves as tea or extract, roots the same

Alternative herbs: chicory, burdock, yellow dock, oregon grape

Cautions and Comments: dandelion leaf has been compared to Lasix(furosemide) in German studies in its diuretic capabilities, however dandelion replaces the potassium normally lost through diuresis.

Dill - *Anethum graveolens*
Parts Used: all aerial parts
Actions: soothes stomach, antimicrobial
Affinities: digestive tract & mouth; urinary tract
Specific Uses: stomach upset, urinary tract infections, gum infections, bad breath.
Availability: supermarket or herb store
Preparation: infusion, poultice, extract, encapsulated, dried bulk
Alternative Herbs: thyme, parsley leaf, couchgrass (urinary)
Cautions & Comments: the poultice or tea can be rubbed onto an animal's gums to reduce bad breath and fight infection.

Echinacea - *E. angustifolia* (*E.purpurea*)
Parts Used: roots, leaves (much weaker)
Actions: immunostimulant, anti-viral, anti-microbial, alterative, anti-bacterial
Affinities: immune system, lymphatic, respiratory
Specific Uses: at the onset of infections
Availability: seed catalogs, nurseries
Preparation: extract, capsules
Alternative herbs: cat's claw, astragalus
Cautions and Comments: please be sure to use organically grown echinacea, as wild stands(wildcrafted) are being wiped-out. It is easy to grow in the garden. It should be used for short periods of time with breaks in between so as not to over-stimulate the immune system. Contraindicated in autoimmune diseases.

Eucalyptus - *Eucalyptus species*
Parts Used: leaves
Actions: astringent, anti-inflammatory, expectorant, antibacterial
Affinities: skin and respiratory
Specific Uses: skin wash for flea bite dermatitis, respiratory decongestant (topical fomentation or steam inhalation)
Availability: herb stores
Preparation: infusion, or commercially-available oil diluted in hot water
Alternative Herbs: juniper, sage, tea tree
Cautions & Comments: the concentrated oil is very strong and may cause contact dermatitis if used undiluted. Not for direct internal use; use sparingly as a rinse.

Eyebright - *Euphrasia species*
Parts Used: flowering plant
Actions: astringent, anti-inflammatory
Affinities: eyes
Specific Uses: conjunctivitis
Availability: herb stores, but we discourage its use
Preparation: diluted infusion or alcohol extract
Alternative Herbs: raspberry, nettle, chamomile, or strawberry leaf
Cautions & Comments: this plant is being over-harvested from its natural habitat. Please use an alternative!

Fennel - Foeniculum species

Parts Used: seed
Actions: expels gas and relieves indigestion, antispasmodic, antimicrobial
Affinities: digestive and respiratory
Specific Uses: chronic or acute gastritis, helps calm coughs, freshens breath.
Availability: supermarket or herb store; easy to grow
Preparation: bulk dried seeds, encapsulated, infusion, glycerin extract
Alternative Herbs: catnip, parsley seed, chamomile, bee balm
Cautions & Comments: safe and effective against fungal infections of the digestive tract. Swab the extract onto the teeth and gums to fight gingivitis and freshen breath. Safe for long term use.

Feverfew - Tanacetum parthenium

Parts Used: aboveground parts
Actions: anti-inflammatory, anti-spasmodic, bitter, vasodilator, relaxant, emmenagogue
Affinities: digestive tract, nervous system, musculo-skeletal
Specific Uses: pain relief
Availability: seed catalogs
Preparation: extract
Alternative herbs: skullcap, bugleweed
Cautions and Comments: not to be used during pregnancy. The flowers contain pyrethrins, and are useful in powder or infusion for discouraging fleas. Very toxic to aquatic organisms.

Garlic - Allium sativuum

Parts Used: bulbs(cloves), below ground portion
Actions: antibiotic, antimicrobial, anti parasitic, antifungal, nutritive, anti-tumor, digestive stimulant
Affinities: respiratory, cardiovascular, immune
Specific Uses: infections, worms, lowering cholesterol
Availability: grocery/health food stores
Preparation: fresh cloves or extracts
Alternative herbs: echinacea (immune system)
Cautions and Comments: if fed in enough quantity, may cause Heinz-body anemia in dogs and cats (cats are more sensitive than dogs). Use sparingly in pet food recipes.

Ginger - Zingiber officinale

Parts Used: root
Actions: vasodilator, soothes stomach ache, circulatory tonic
Affinities: circulatory system, skin, digestive tract
Specific Uses: helps relieve nausea; motion sickness. Circulatory disorders.
Ginger warms the body and acts as a potentiating carrier when combined with other herbs.
Availability: supermarkets and herb stores
Preparation: capsules, fresh root, dried powder.
Alternative Herbs: cayenne, yarrow

Cautions & Comments: ginger acts as a carrier for other herbs, and combines particularly well in expectorant formulations, with herbs such as mullein, goldenrod, and yarrow.

Ginkgo - *Ginkgo biloba*
Parts Used: leaves
Actions: antioxidant, vasodilator, anti-inflammatory, stimulant, anti-clotting
Affinities: cardiovascular, nervous, brain tissue, genito-urinary, respiratory
Specific Uses: deafness, prevents platelet aggregation that can lead to blockage of arteries
Availability: herb catalogs; slow growing, requires large quantities of water to grow
Preparation: extract
Alternative herbs: peppermint
Cautions and Comments: do not use during pregnancy or lactation, or for prolonged periods of time in high doses.

Goldenrod - *Solidago species*
Parts Used: aerial parts of the flowering plant
Actions: astringent, kidney tonic, diuretic
Affinities: respiratory, urinary, kidneys
Specific Uses: reduces mucus secretions in bronchi, strengthens kidney functions
Availability: a common weed
Preparation: extract, dried herb, infusion
Alternative herbs: mullein, coltsfoot (respiratory); dandelion, alfalfa (urinary and kidneys)
Cautions and Comments: should not be used in pre-existing kidney disease. Highly allergenic... use with caution at first. Commonly sprayed with herbicides; do not gather from roadways or cultivated areas.

Goldenseal - *Hydrastis canadensis*
Parts Used: roots
Actions: antipathogenic, anti-catarrhal, bitter, hepatic, antiseptic, laxative
Affinities: mucous membranes, digestive, respiratory, musculo-skeletal, respiratory, skin
Specific Uses: infections; bronchial inflammation
Availability: organically grown, herb and health food stores
Preparation: extract or infusion
Alternative herbs: Oregon Grape root(Berberis repens)
Cautions and Comments: *please... use organically grown only,* as it is compromised in the wild(wildcrafted), or use Oregon grape in its place. Do not use in cases of low blood sugar, or low blood pressure, do not use during pregnancy. Should not be used continuously for more than ten days, as it is very oxidizing and may over-stimulate liver function. Very bitter tasting.

Grindelia - *Grindelia squarrosa*
Parts Used: leaf bud and flower
Actions: anti-spasmodic, expectorant, hypotensive
Affinities: respiratory, skin, cardiac

Specific Uses: spasmodic coughs
Availability: seed catalogs
Preparation: extract
Alternative herbs: mullein leaf, coltsfoot
Cautions and Comments: due to relaxing effect on heart and blood pressure there may be a reduction in blood pressure. For short term use only.

Hawthorn - *Crataegus species*

Parts Used: berries, flowering branches (leaves intact)
Actions: circulatory moderator
Affinities: cardiovascular, digestive
Specific Uses: low OR high blood pressure, coronary irregularities, heart deficiencies
Availability: herb catalogs, health food stores
Preparation: extract
Alternative herbs: garlic
Cautions and Comments: combines well with garlic and dandelion for chronic heart conditions and vascular disorders. Seek professional guidance in these circumstances.

Hops - *Humulus lupulus*

Parts Used: strobiles(flowers)
Actions: sedative, digestive, bitter, astringent
Affinities: nervous system, digestive system
Specific Uses: sedative; to aid digestion
Availability: herb catalogs, health food stores
Preparation: extract; infusion
Alternative herbs: oatstraw, valerian, skullcap, chamomile
Cautions and Comments: deaths of dogs--- especially greyhounds and other breeds which may be predisposed to malignant hyperthermia, have been attributed to excessive consumption of hop material which has been discarded after beer making. No toxicity has been noted with the use of medicinal preparations of hops. Use only as directed.

Horsetail - *Equisetum arvense*

Parts Used: aboveground portions
Actions: anti-inflammatory, diuretic, astringent, anti-hemorrhagic, vulnerary(wound healing)
Affinities: kidneys, lungs, liver, connective tissues and bones.
Specific Uses: connective tissue injuries and fractures, diuretic, urinary tract disorders, including incontinence.
Availability: herb stores; widely distributed in the wild.
Preparation: extract or decoction
Alternative herbs: couchgrass, dandelion, raspberry leaf, marshmallow
Cautions and Comments: should not be used in hypertension or cardiac cases. Should not be used during pregnancy. May irritate the urinary tract if used over long term. This plant pulls heavy metals and toxins from its environment... do not gather near road ways or from contaminated soil.

Juniper - *Juniperis species*
Parts Used: berries, leaves
Actions: lowers blood sugar levels, diuretic, antimicrobial
Affinities: skin, kidneys, urinary tract
Specific Uses: antiseptic/astringent skin wash, urinary tract infections, diabetes
Availability: herb stores, supermarket, easy to grow landscape shrub
Preparation: diluted extract or decoction of leaves and berries
Alternative Herbs: sage, couchgrass, uva-ursi, huckleberry leaf,
Cautions & Comments: do not use in pre-existing kidney disease. The leaves are strongly astringent, and preparations should be dilute. One or two berries can be ground and added to food for urinary tract infections. May cause urinary and kidney irritation if used over an extended period. Consult a veterinarian for use in diabetic animals.

Licorice - *Glycyrrhiza glabra*
Parts Used: root
Actions: expectorant, alterative, demulcent, anti-inflammatory, adrenal agent, mild laxative, liver tonic
Affinities: respiratory, digestive, endocrine
Specific Uses: hypoglycemia, coughs, Addison's disease. Protects liver from toxins.
Availability: herb catalogs, health food stores
Preparation: extract
Alternative herbs: yucca, alfalfa
Cautions and Comments: not recommended for those with high blood pressure which is due to water retention, and for long-term use a potassium supplement and diuretic (such as Dandelion leaf) should be added.

Marshmallow - *Althea officinalis*
Parts Used: roots
Actions: soothing and protecting to internal and external tissues, diuretic, nutritive, vulnerary(wound healing), antimicrobial
Affinities: digestive, urinary, respiratory
Specific Uses: cystitis, enteritis, diarrhea, urinary incontinence, FUS, bladder stones. Very good to help with passage of furballs and minor intestinal blockages.
Availability: herb catalogs, health food stores
Preparation: low-alcohol extract, tea
Alternative herbs: plantain (psyllium), slippery elm
Cautions and Comments: may slow the absorption of some drugs. Use only low-alcohol extracts. Extracts which contain more than 20% alcohol may cause digestive upset in animals.

Milk Thistle - *Silybum marianum*
Parts Used: ripe seeds
Actions: tonic, nutritive, cholagogue, demulcent
Affinities: digestive(liver), urinary(kidneys), spleen, skin
Specific Uses: leptospirosis, parvovirus, hepatitis, jaundice, pancreatitis, hypoglycemia,

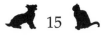

recovery from drug use or anesthesia.
Availability: herb catalogs, health food stores
Preparation: alcohol extract of seed (not soluble in water or glycerin).
Alternative herbs: licorice
Cautions and Comments: may increase some liver enzymes if used where there is no on-going stress to the liver. Has been used to antidote Amanita mushroom poisoning when given early enough. May slow liver functions if used excessively.

Mullein - *Verbascum thapsus*
Parts Used: roots, leaves, flowers
Actions: demulcent, anti-inflammatory
Affinities: urinary(roots), lungs(leaves), ears(flowers)
Specific Uses: coughs(leaves), urinary incontinence(roots), ear mites/infections(flowers in oil)
Availability: herb catalogs, health food stores
Preparation: extract, infusion, or oil infusion(ears)
Alternative herbs: coltsfoot, grindelia, garlic, marshmallow, horsetail
Cautions and Comments: the seeds of this plant may be toxic if crushed and ingested. The flowers are high in rotenone; a substance which is deadly to aquatic life.

Nettles - *Urtica dioica*
Parts Used: leaves
Actions: tonic, nutritive, alterative, astringent, expectorant, diuretic, antihistamine
Affinities: genito-urinary, respiratory, blood, skin
Specific Uses: flushing urinary system, skin and eye washes (conjunctivitis), an excellent nutritional supplement, provides systemic support against allergens.
Availability: herb stores, widely distributed in wild
Preparation: extract or infusion
Alternative herbs: Raspberry leaf, chamomile, dandelion, oxeye daisy
Cautions and Comments: touching the live plant will result in a painful, blistering sting. Thorough drying or cooking neutralizes the toxic constituents. Use this plant before it flowers... mature plants contain gritty particles that can irritate the kidneys.

Oatstraw - *Avena sativa*
Parts Used: seed and straw
Actions: tonic, nervine, antidepressant, nutritive, demulcent, vulnerary(wound healing)
Affinities: nervous system, circulatory, skin
Specific Uses: tonic and anti-inflammatory for epilepsy, twitching, tremors and paralysis
Availability: herb catalogs, health food stores, widely distributed weed
Preparation: extract or infusion
Alternative herbs: chamomile, valerian, skullcap, hops
Cautions and Comments: wild plants may have been sprayed with an herbicide.

Oregon Grape - *Berberis (Mahonia) spp.*
Parts Used: roots

Actions: alterative, cholagogue, hepatic, tonic, laxative
Affinities: digestive, skin, blood, lymphatic, genitourinary
Specific Uses: use in place of Goldenseal when possible. Often useful in treating chronic constipation.
Availability: herb catalogs, health food stores
Preparation: extract or infusion (water or oil)
Alternative herbs: organically-grown goldenseal
Cautions and Comments: should not be used in acute liver disease. Do not use in pregnant or lactating animals.

Oxeye Daisy - *Chrysanthemum leucanthemum*

Parts Used: above-ground parts
Actions: anti-bacterial, anti-fungal, astringent, diuretic, hemostatic, antihistamine
Affinities: respiratory, skin
Specific Uses: over-concentrated, acidic urine, watery discharges, allergies
Availability: herb seed catalogs, widely distributed weed
Preparation: infusion
Alternative herbs: nettle
Cautions and Comments: the dried flowers can be crushed and spread about to discourage fleas, due to its pyrethrin content. Suspect the presence of herbicides when harvesting.

Parsley - *Petroselinum crispum*

Parts Used: foliage, seeds, root
Actions: diuretic, carminative, nutritive, anti-rheumatic
Affinities: urinary system
Specific Uses: the root is a good diuretic for rheumatoid arthritis. The leaf infusion helps reduce bad breath. Seeds help relieve digestive gas.
Availability: seed catalogs(easy to grow), health food/herb stores
Preparation: fresh juice or infusion
Alternative herbs: fennel, bee balm, catnip, dandelion, alfalfa
Cautions and Comments: not to be used in pregnancy in medicinal quantities, or during kidney disease.

Pennyroyal - *Hedeoma pulegioides*

Parts used: foliage
Actions: flea repellent; astringent
Affinities: skin
Specific Uses: flea repellent (but not recommended).
Availability: herb stores, nurseries, easy to grow
Preparation: infusion of dried herb; oil.
Alternative Herbs: yarrow, oxeye daisy, sage, wormwood
Cautions and Comments: Any quantity of this herb may be highly toxic in animals; especially cats... always avoid internal use; especially during pregnancy. The undiluted oil may cause contact dermatitis, and should never be ingested. We recommend against the use of this plant.

Psyllium/Plantain - *Plantago species*
Parts Used: seeds, seed heads, foliage, roots
Actions: soothes and protects tissues, both internally and externally; mildly astringent
Affinities: skin and digestive tract
Specific Uses: psyllium seed is effective for acute cases of constipation. The leaf and/or root extract is useful for irritations of the skin and digestive tract. The leaf poultice is a soothing field application for insect bites and stings.
Availability: herb stores; a widely distributed group of weeds. All species are useful.
Preparation: infusion, extract, dried herb, poultice
Alternative Herbs: marshmallow, slippery elm
Cautions & Comments: Suspect the presence of herbicides when harvesting.

Pumpkin Seed
Parts Used: raw, unsalted, dried seed.
Actions: helps expel tapeworms
Affinities: digestive tract
Specific Uses: tapeworms
Availability: health food stores
Preparation: grind and put a liberal amount into your pet's food— or feed whole, as a treat.
Alternative Herbs: black walnut, garlic.
Cautions & Comments: combines well with black walnut and garlic. Expect one or two months of feeding to see desired results.

Red Clover - *Trifolium pratense*
Parts Used: flowering tops
Actions: alterative, diuretic, nutritive, antitumor
Affinities: liver and blood
Specific Uses: bronchitis, cysts, all debilitating diseases, historically used for cancer
Availability: seed catalogs, herb/health food stores
Preparation: infusion or extract
Alternative herbs: alfalfa, dandelion, burdock
Cautions and Comments: do not use in clotting disorders or in the presence of internal or external bleeding. This plant contains the compound *coumarin*, which has blood-thinning qualities.

Red Raspberry - *Rubus idaeus*
Parts Used: leaves(thoroughly dried)
Actions: astringent, tonic, antispasmodic
Affinities: genito-urinary tract, digestive, eyes
Specific Uses: strengthening and toning to uterus during pregnancy; astringent skin and eye wash. Useful and safe in the treatment of conjunctivitis and soreness of moist tissues.
Availability: seed catalogs, herb/health food stores
Preparation: extract or tea
Alternative herbs: nettle, strawberry leaf

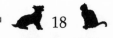

Cautions and Comments: leaves need to be thoroughly dried, as they assume a temporary, mild toxicity when they first wilt.

Rose - *rosa species*

Parts Used: fruits (hips), flowers, leaves, bark
Actions: nutritive, astringent, antimicrobial, helps speed healing of wounds
Affinities: skin and digestive system
Specific Uses: the hips are very high in vitamin C. The rest of this plant is useful in skin washes; for treatment of irritations, insect bites and stings, and burns. The root bark is the strongest part. Flower petals can be used as a field dressing for minor wounds.
Availability: all varieties of rose are useful.
Preparation: decoction (bark), infusion (leaves and hips), direct application or poultice (flowers)
Alternative Herbs: raspberry leaf, chamomile, juniper, nettle.
Cautions & Comments: suspect herbicides on wild stands of this plant.

Rosemary - *Rosmarinus officinalis*

Parts Used: leaves, stems, flowers
Actions: antimicrobial, astringent, sedative, expels gas, circulatory stimulant
Affinities: circulatory, digestive, and nervous systems
Specific Uses: digestive disorders attributable to nervousness.
Availability: herb stores, supermarket, easy to grow.
Preparation: infusion or extract
Alternative Herbs: chamomile, bee balm, catnip, skullcap
Cautions & Comments: as a sedative it is similar in action to chamomile, but stronger.

Sage - *Salvia species*

Parts Used: foliage
Actions: antibacterial, astringent, anti-inflammatory
Affinities: digestive & skin
Specific Uses: skin, mouth, or throat infections, repels fleas
Availability: herb or food stores, nurseries, seed catalogs; easy to grow
Preparation: infusion or poultice
Alternative Herbs: juniper or wormwood (skin); Oregon Grape (mouth)

Senna - *Cassia senna*

Parts Used: dried fruit pods
Actions: cathartic (a strong laxative)
Affinities: digestive system
Specific Uses: acute constipation, when all other measures have failed
Availability: herb stores
Preparation: infusion, encapsulated
Alternative Herbs: turkey rhubarb, cascara sagrada, oregon grape (a more holistic choice)
Cautions & Comments: in general, we dislike using this herb. It is very harsh, often causing abdominal griping and cramping, and severe diarrhea when used. Senna is not to

be viewed as a holistic approach to the treatment of constipation or worms, and should only be employed as a last resort; under the guidance of a professional.

St. John's Wort - *Hypericum perforatum*

Parts Used: flowering tops and leaves
Actions: anti-inflammatory, astringent, diuretic, vulnerary, sedative analgesic, antiseptic
Affinities: nervous system, musculo-skeletal, urinary, skin
Specific Uses: neuralgia, rheumatism, arthritis, slipped disc, nerve injuries. An excellent healing agent for minor wounds and burns.
Availability: herb/health food stores
Preparation: infusion, oil, or extract
Alternative herbs: catnip, comfrey, chaparral, skullcap, feverfew.
Cautions and Comments: caution should be used when taken internally in light-skinned, fair-haired subjects, due to possible photosensitivity; particularly cows, horses, and other large herbivores.

Shepherd's Purse - *Capsella bursa-pastoris*

Parts Used: entire flowering plant.
Actions: diuretic, uterine stimulant, astringent, hypotensive, slows bleeding
Affinities: genito-urinary tract, cardiovascular
Specific Uses: difficult placenta delivery, toning the uterus, postpartum bleeding, arthritis
Availability: seed catalogs, health/herb stores
Preparation: extract or tea
Alternative herbs: parsley root, dandelion
Cautions and Comments: do not use in the presence of blood-clotting disorders.

Skullcap - *Scutellaria sp.*

Parts Used: aerial parts
Actions: nerve tonic, sedative, anti-spasmodic
Affinities: nervous, musculo-skeletal
Specific Uses: epilepsy, seizures, spinal problems, neuritis, twitching, restlessness,
Availability: seed catalogs, herb/health food stores
Preparation: extract, infusion
Alternative herbs: oatstraw, valerian, rosemary
Cautions and Comments: do not use in predisposed or existing liver disease.

Slippery Elm - *Ulmus fulva*

Parts Used: inner bark of the tree
Actions: demulcent, astringent
Affinities: digestive tract & respiratory
Specific Uses: a classic remedy for acute diarrhea, stomach ulcers, constipation, colitis, sore throat, coughs, wounds, abscesses.
Availability: herb and health food stores
Preparation: extract, infusion

Alternative herbs: marshmallow, rose, psyllium.
Cautions and Comments: combines well with red clover, burdock, yellow dock for elimination of excess waste from the liver and digestive tract.

Thyme - *Thymus species*
Parts Used: leaves, stems, flowers
Actions: antimicrobial, expels gas from the digestive tract, astringent
Affinities: digestive tract, mouth, skin, respiratory
Specific Uses: an excellent disinfectant for the mouth and gums. Works similar to chamomile in the stomach, but with greater infection-fighting capabilities. Useful for asthma in a steam.
Availability: herb store, supermarket
Preparation: infusion; extract.
Alternative Herbs: parsley, chamomile, fennel
Cautions & Comments: can be swabbed onto the teeth and gums to fight gingivitis.

Turmeric - *Curcuma longa*
Parts Used: roots
Actions: antibacterial, liver tonic, anti parasitic, anti-tumor
Affinities: liver, blood, digestive tract
Specific Uses: chronic constipation associated with poor liver function, may be useful against giardia and other parasites. Protects the liver against damaging toxins.
Availability: herb store and supermarket
Preparation: extract or encapsulated
Alternative Herbs: oregon grape (parasites), milk thistle or licorice (liver)
Cautions & Comments: studies conducted at Rutgers University have shown that turmeric helps prevent tumor growth in animals.

Turkey Rhubarb - *Rheum palmatum*
Parts Used: root
Actions: antibiotic, antimicrobial, anti-tumor
Affinities: digestive tract
Specific Uses: digestive, liver tonic, appetite stimulant
Availability: herb/health food stores
Preparation: extract or infusion
Alternative herbs: cascara sagrada, oregon grape
Cautions and Comments: not to be used in pregnancy, lactation, newborns, or kidney problems. Use in small doses to *aid* digestive functions, not to replace them. Continuous use of this and other herbal laxatives may cause systemic dependency.

Valerian - *Valeriana officinalis*
Parts Used: root and rhizome
Actions: sedative, anodyne(pain reliever), antispasmodic, carminative, hypotensive
Affinities: nervous system, digestive
Specific Uses: muscle spasms, pain, nervousness, anti-convulsive, curb aggression

Availability: herb and health food stores
Preparation: extract
Alternative herbs: chamomile, catnip, skullcap, oatstraw, hops.
Cautions and Comments: should not be given in large doses for long periods of time, as it may cause stomach upset or lethargy. May have reverse (stimulant) effects in some subjects. If this happens, try an alternative herb.

Wild Cherry - *Prunus virginiana*

Parts Used: dried bark
Actions: respiratory sedative, narcotic
Affinities: respiratory
Specific Uses: respiratory sedative in acute conditions, kennel cough
Availability: herb/health food stores
Preparation: extract, syrup
Alternative herbs: licorice, mullein, grindelia, yarrow, slippery elm, marshmallow
Cautions and Comments: avoid during pregnancy, and do not use the seeds or leaves of the plant. This herb suppresses cough response mechanisms in the brain— a function which serves symptomatic, not holistic purposes.

Wormwood - *Artemisia species*

Parts Used: leaves, stems, and flowers
Actions: antimicrobial, repels insects, fleas, and parasites
Affinities: skin
Specific Uses: topical applications... antiseptic skin washes and to repel fleas
Availability: herb stores, nurseries, easy to grow, widespread in the wild
Preparation: powdered herb, infusion.
Alternative Herbs: sage, juniper, thyme
Cautions & Comments: all members of the Artemisia genus are useful. Although wormwood has earned a reputation as an effective wormer, we discourage its internal use because of its potential to damage the liver. If it can kill a tapeworm, it can't be good for your animal!

Yellow Dock - *Rumex crispus*

Parts Used: root
Actions: alterative, cholagogue, laxative, astringent, nutritive
Affinities: digestive, eliminative, blood
Specific Uses: anemia, ulcers, constipation and liver congestion; a traditional treatment for heavy metal toxicity.
Availability: seed catalogs, herb/health food stores
Preparation: extract, infusion
Alternative herbs: dandelion, burdock, red clover, alfalfa, chicory.
Cautions and Comments: may cause gastrointestinal upset if taken in large quantities, and may deplete vitamin B-1 from the body if used over an extended period of time.

Yucca - *Yucca species*

Parts Used: root

Actions: anti-inflammatory, anti-rheumatic, cleansing

Affinities: musclo-skeletal

Specific Uses: arthritis, hip dysplasia, joint injuries, and to increase absorption of nutrients in the small intestine.

Availability: herb stores, easy to grow

Preparation: extract or powdered herb

Alternative herbs: licorice

Cautions and Comments: excessive, long-term use can have a reverse effect in the intestine, slowing the absorption of certain fat-soluble vitamins. Large doses may be irritating to the stomach lining; causing nausea and vomiting.

NOTES

Glycerin-based Compound Formulations

Following is a list of low-alcohol, glycerin-based formulation suggestions that may be used for dogs and cats. Alcohol tinctures work too, but animals hate the taste and it can be very difficult to administer an appropriate dosage. Generally, a compound formula contains one or two "base herbs" that represent the primary focus of the formula, and act as buffering carriers for other, perhaps more potent, elements of the formula. The base herbs constitute the largest percentage of the formula, and are usually comprised of gentle, tonic herbs that will act to strengthen the body's ability to heal itself. Herbs that act to releive only the uncomfortable symptoms of disease, or those associated with a risk of side effects, are usually proportioned in smaller percentages of the formula. Remember--- the goal of herbal therapy is not just symptomatic relief, but to help the body heal itself by addressing the underlying causes of disease. Keep the primary focus of your compound formulas on strengthening the body, and nature will amaze you. For example, the *Alfalfa/Yucca Blend* contains mostly alfalfa and burdock extracts, which act together to provide mild liver support while providing mild gentle anti-inflammatory qualities and predictable diuretic actions. Licorice and yucca are much stronger, and act more directly in their anti-inflammatory actions, but also have potential side-effects when used in long-term applications (see licorice and yucca in the A to Z section). When combined in lesser proportions with the alfalfa and burdock, risk of adverse side effects are significantly reduced, but the actions of the yucca and licorice remain intact to provide immediate, symptomatic relief while the tonic, base herbs do their work at the root of the problem. The result: a synergistic combination of herbs that work together to achieve a holistic, curative approach toward the systemic imbalances of arthritic or traumatic joint diseases, and... relief of the painful symptoms.

Determining exactly what and how much of each herb to include in a compound formulation requires knowledge and experience that cannot be conveyed in this book. Dosage will vary according to the focus of therapy, the specific array and percentages of ingredient herbs, and the overall potency of the formula. If in doubt about your ability to formulate a compound that is safe and effective, consult your holistic veterinarian, or refer to the suggestions of reputable product manufacturers to determine dosage.

Alfalfa/Yucca Blend

Contains: Alfalfa (Medicago sativa), Yucca Root (Yucca spp.), Burdock (Arctium spp.), Licorice (Glycyrrhiza glabra), and Shepherd's Purse (Capsella bursa-pastoris) in a vegetable glycerine and water base.

Indications: Arthritis and other rheumatoid conditions which are accompanied by pain, swelling, or stiffness of the joints. Also good for recovery from joint injuries.

Actions: Nutritive, anti-inflammatory, and diuretic... to help the body cope with the pain of arthritis and rheumatism while tonifying the liver and kidneys to help eliminate excess waste materials and water from the joints.

Method of Application: Liquid extract; administered directly into the mouth or onto food just before each feeding.

Starting Dose and Duration: Up to 12 drops for cats; up to 12 drops per 20 lbs. of body weight; for dogs, 2-3x per day; 5 days on, 2 off for duration of therapy.

Comments and Cautions: May cause water retention or stomach upset with long term use in some animals. Do not use in animals with pre-existing blood clotting disorders, in pregnant animals, or in the presence of fluid retention disorders.

Coltsfoot/Wild Cherry Blend

Contains: Coltsfoot (Petasites spp.), Mullein leaf (Verbascum thapsis), Grindelia (Grindelia squarrosa), Slippery Elm (Ulmus vulva), Wild Cherry bark (Prunus virginiana), and Licorice (Glycyrrhiza glabra), in a vegetable glycerine and water base.

Indications: Unproductive coughs which are due to particulate irritation, bacterial or viral infection.

Actions: Soothes and relieves coughs and irritation of the respiratory tract due to the expectorant, anti-inflammatory, and antispasmodic actions of these herbs.

Method of Application: Liquid extract; administered directly into the mouth between meals.

Starting Dose and Duration: Up to 12 drops for cats; up to12 drops per 20 lbs. of body weight for dogs; 2-3x per day; 5 days on, 2 off, not to exceed 14 days total.

Cautions and Comments: Excessive, long term use may lead to liver dysfunction or water retention. If a cough persists for more than a few days, consult a holistic veterinarian.

Constitutional Blend (also known as the 'Essicat' formula)

Contains: Yellow Dock (Rumex crispus), Burdock (Arctium spp.), Dandelion (Taraxacum off.), Slippery Elm (Ulmus fulva), and Turkey Rhubarb (Rheum palmatum) in a vegetable glycerine and water base.

Indications: This is a traditional rapid- detox formulation that has been used in animals and humans for decades, in treatment of cancer, heavy metal toxicity, and various forms of liver deficiency.

Actions: Soothing, lubricating, and protecting within the digestive tract. Stimulates liver function and digestion to aid in the elimination of toxic compounds and excess systemic waste from the body. May be used as a laxative to help with chronic constipation.

Method of Application: Liquid extract; administered directly into the mouth, 15 minutes before meals.

Starting Dose and Duration: Up to 12 drops for cats; up to 12 drops per 20 lbs. of body weight for dogs; 2-3x per day; 5 days on, 2 off; not to exceed two weeks. After two weeks, this formula can be followed by long term use of "Detox/Allergy Blend" (below).

Cautions and Comments: Long term use may cause vitamin B1 deficiencies, and may irritate the liver and kidneys. Do not use in animals with pre-existing liver or kidney disease.

Detox/Allergy Blend

Contains: Burdock (Arctium spp.), Dandelion (Taraxacum off.), Milk Thistle (Silybum marianum), Red Clover (Trifolium pratense), Alfalfa (Medicago sativa), and Licorice (Glycyrrhiza glabra) in a vegetable glycerine and water base.

Indications: Chronic flea or seasonal allergies; itchy, flaky skin conditions.

Actions: Assists the metabolic functions of the body during acute or chronic cases of allergy or other systemic imbalances related to liver dysfunction, excess toxicity, or intoler-

ance to allergens.

Method of Application: Liquid extract; administered directly into the mouth or onto food just before each feeding.

Starting Dose and Duration: Up to 12 drops for cats; 12 drops per 20 lbs. of body weight for dogs; 2-3x per day; 5 days on, 2 off for duration of therapy. safe for long term use.

Cautions and Comments: Provided that licorice is not a disprortionately large portion of the compound, this is a safe, well-balanced formula that can be used over extended periods in most dogs or cats... but always monitor your pet for allergies or sensitivity before using *any* herbal preparation.

Feverfew/Skullcap Blend

Contains: Feverfew (Tanacetum parthenium), Skullcap (Scutellaria laterifolia), Valerian (Valeriana off.), and Licorice (Glycyrrhiza glabra) in a vegetable glycerine and water base.

Indications: To help relieve pain in post-surgical, and post-traumatic situations. Can be used for any physically painful situation.

Actions: Anti-inflammatory, and calming.

Method of Application: Liquid extract; administered directly into the mouth or onto food just before each feeding.

Starting Dose and Duration: Up to 12 drops for cats; up to 12 drops per 20 lbs. of body weight for dogs; 2-3x per day; 5 days on, 2 off for up to two weeks.

Cautions and Comments: May cause stomach upset in some animals, if used in excessive doses. Do not use in pregnant animals. Feverfew is toxic to aquatic life forms, but safe in dogs and cats.

Goldenseal/Echinacea Blend

Contains: Goldenseal (Hydrastis canadensis), Echinacea (Echinacea purpurea), Alfalfa (Medicago sativa), Garlic (Allium sativum), and Blue-Green Algae (Alphanizomenon flos-aquae) in a vegetable glycerine and water base.

Indications: A systemic approach to bacterial, fungal, or minor parasitic infections. Especially effective at the onset of infectious disease. Very useful for infections of the mouth and urinary tract.

Actions: Optimizes the immune-supporting effectiveness of Echinacea while helping to fight bacterial infection in the tissues it contacts. Tonifying to natural body functions.

Method of Application: Liquid extract; administered directly into the mouth, on the animal's food, or in drinking water; or topically onto the affected area.

Starting Dose and Duration: Up to 12 drops for cats; up to 12 drops per 20 lbs. of body weight for dogs; 2-3x per day; 5 days on, 2 off for up to two weeks.

Cautions and Comments: Do not use in animals with pre-existing autoimmune disease. Do not use in pregnant or lactating animals.

Senior Blend

Contains: Alfalfa (Medicago sativa), Dandelion (Taraxacum off.), Milk Thistle (Silybum marianum), Ginkgo (Ginkgo biloba), Hawthorn (Crataegus spp.), Oatstraw (Avena sativa), Garlic (Allium sativum), and Marshmallow (Althea off.) in vegetable glycerine and water base.

Indications: For older companion animals as an overall nutritive and soothing tonic that covers body, mind, and spirit.

Actions: Provides gentle tonic support to the cardiovascular system, digestive tract, and liver.

Method of Application: Liquid extract; administered directly into the mouth, on the animal's food, or in drinking water.

Starting Dose and Duration: Up to 12 drops for cats; up to 12 drops per 20 lbs. of body weight for dogs; 2-3x per day; 5 days on, 2 off.

Cautions and Comments: Safe for long term use.

Tinkle Tonic (a cute name for 'Urinary Formula')

Contains: Couchgrass (Agropyron repens), Echinacea (Echinacea purpurea), Marshmallow (Althea off.), Dandelion (Taraxacum officinalis), and Horsetail (Equisetum arvense) in a vegetable glycerine and water base.

Indications: Useful for Feline Urological Syndrome. A soothing, tonifying, antimicrobial, and anti-inflammatory to relieve the symptoms of any minor urinary tract problem.

Actions: Anti-inflammatory, soothing, and protecting to the urinary tract.

Method of Application: Liquid extract; administered directly into the mouth or in drinking water.

Starting Dose and Duration: Up to 12 drops for cats; up to 12 drops per 20 lbs. of body weight for dogs; 2-3x per day; 5 days on, 2 off... until symptoms are relieved, or to a maximum of two weeks.

Cautions and Comments: Seek the advice of a holistic veterinarian before using in animals with kidney disease.

Tranquility Blend

Contains: Valerian (Valeriana off.), Skullcap (Scutellaria laterifolia), Hops (Humulus lupulus), and Oatstraw (Avena sativa) in a vegetable glycerine and water base.

Indications: For acute anxiety disorders and stress due to lifestyle changes; these four calming nervines are safe, gentle, and effective.

Actions: Mildly sedative; calming.

Method of Application: Liquid extract; administered directly into the mouth, on the animal's food; preferably followed by a drink of water.

Starting Dose and Duration: Up to 12 drops for cats; up to 12 drops per 20 lbs. of body weight for dogs; 2-3x per day; for up to five 5 days on, three off.

Cautions and Comments: may have a reverse effect in some animals. May cause stomach upset in some animals; especially if administered without drinking water.

Herb Remedy Cross-reference

The following chart will help you find the correct herbal approach toward your animal's needs. Please bear in mind that this is only a partial list of existing possiblities, and it does not serve as a substitute for the care and advice of a veterinary professional. To use this chart, match your pet's ailments as closely as possible to the conditions listed **(in bold)** below. Then, read about each suggested herb in the *A to Z* section of this book to choose which choices are most appropriate for your companion. The authors have included suggestions for use of a specific compound formula *(in italics)*, and have noted what they regard as the best single herb choices **(in bold)** under each heading.

Addison's Disease
 Licorice

Allergies
 Detox/Allergy Blend
 Goldenrod
 Nettle
 Oregon Grape
 Oxeye Daisy
 Yucca

Alterative
 Detox/Allergy Blend
 Alfalfa
 Burdock
 Oregon Grape
 Red Clover
 Turmeric
 Yellow Dock

Antibacterial
 Goldenseal/Echinacea
 Garlic
 Goldenseal
 Oxeye Daisy

Antibiotic
 Goldenseal/Echinacea
 Echinacea
 Garlic

Antifungal
 Garlic
 Goldenseal
 Oregon Grape
 Oxeye Daisy

Anti-inflammatory
 Internally
 Licorice
 Yucca
 Feverfew
 Hawthorn
 Mullein
 Oatstraw
 Willow
 Yarrow

 Mucous membranes
 Oxeye Daisy
 Externally
 Oxeye Daisy
 Yarrow

Antimicrobial/anti-septic
 Goldenseal/Echinacea
 Echinacea
 Garlic
 Oxeye Daisy
 Turkey Rhubarb
 Willow

Antioxidant
 Alfalfa
 Ginkgo

Anti-protozoan
 (Giardia)
 Goldenseal/Echinacea
 Goldenseal
 Oregon Grape
 Garlic

Antispasmodic
 Chamomile
 Coltsfoot
 Feverfew
 Grindelia
 Hawthorn
 Valerian

Antiviral
 St. John's Wort
 Echinacea

Arthritis
 Alfalfa/Yucca Blend
 Detox/Allergy Blend
 Alfalfa
 Nettle
 Yucca
 Burdock
 Dandelion
 Shepherd's Purse

Astringent
 Red Raspberry leaf
 Willow

Birthing
 Nettle
 Shepherd's Purse
 Yarrow

Blood Pressure
 Hawthorn (lowers
 or increases)
 Garlic
 Grindelia
 Valerian
 (lowers)

Bronchitis
 Coltsfoot/Wild Cherry
 Slippery Elm
 Chamomile
 Grindelia
 Mullein
 Red Clover
 Wild Cherry bark

Burns (minor)
 Aloe
 Comfrey
 Calendula
 St. John's Wort
 Rose

Carminative
 (gas/indigestion)
 Catnip
 Chamomile
 Parsley
 Fennel
 Dill

Circulatory/Heart
 Senior Blend
 Hawthorn
 Garlic
 Ginger
 Ginkgo

Constipation
 Constitutional Blend
 Dandelion
 Oregon Grape
 Slippery Elm
 Yellow Dock

Coughing
Coltsfoot/Wild Cherry
  Grindelia
  Licorice
  Wild Cherry bark

Diabetes
  Juniper
  Dandelion
  Nettle

Diarrhea
  Slippery Elm
  Goldenseal
  Marshmallow

Digestive Upset
  Chamomile
  Feverfew
  Hops
  Turkey Rhubarb

Diuretic
Detox/Allergy Blend
Tinkle Tonic
  Dandelion leaf
  Burdock
  Cleavers
  Couchgrass
  Horsetail
  Nettle
  Oxeye Daisy
  Parsley
  Red Clover
  Shepherd's Purse

Epilepsy
  Skullcap
  Oatstraw
  Valerian

Eyes *(conjuctivitis)*
  Oxeye Daisy
  Red Raspberry leaf
  Nettles
  Chamomile

Fevers
  Oxeye Daisy
  Willow
  Yarrow

Fleas
Detox?Allergy Blend
  Garlic
  Eucalyptus
  Rosemary
  Juniper

Gastroenteritis
  Oregon Grape
  Yarrow

Gingivitis/Breath
  Thyme
  Parsley
  Fennel
  Dill
  Rosemary

**Hematuria (blood in
urine)**
Tinkle Tonic
  Couchgrass
  Nettle
  Oxeye Daisy
  Shepherd's Purse

Hemostatic
  Oxeye Daisy
  Red Raspberry leaf
  Shepherd'sPurse

Hyperthyroidism
  Bugleweed

Hypothyroidism
  Licorice

Immunostimulant
  Cat's Claw
  Echinacea
  Garlic
  Licorice
  Marshmallow

Kidneys
  Dandelion lf & rt
  Goldenrod
  Horsetail
  Shepherd's Purse

Leptospirosis
  Milk Thistle

Liver
Detox/Allergy Blend
Constitutional Blend
  Dandelion root
  Licorice
  Milk Thistle
  Oregon Grape
  Red Clover
  Turkey Rhubarb
  Turmeric
  Yellow Dock

Nutritive
  Alfalfa
  Garlic
  Horsetail
  Nettle
  Parsley
  Slippery Elm

Pain
Feverfew/Skullcap
  Valerian
  Bugleweed

Pancreatitis
  Milk Thistle

Parvovirus
  Milk Thistle

Post Surgery
Detox/Allergy
Feverfew/Skullcap
  Burdock
  Dandelion
  Comfrey (topical)
  Aloe (topical)
  Milk Thistle
  Nettle

Sedative
Tranquility Blend
  Chamomile
  Catnip
  Hawthorn
  Hops
  Lemon Balm
  Skullcap
  Valerian

Skin; itchy/flaky
Detox/Allergy Blend
Constitutional Blend
  Burdock
  Calendula
  Chaparral
  Dandelion
  Oats
  Red Clover
  Red Raspberry leaf
  Yellow Dock
  Yucca

Stomach irritation
  Alfalfa
  Catnip
  Slippery Elm

Urinary tract
Tinkle Tonic
  Alfalfa
  Cornsilk
  Cleavers
  Cornsilk
  Couchgrass
  Dill
  Marshmallow
  Nettle
  Oxeye Daisy
  Uva ursi

Vaccinosis
Detox/Allergy Blend

Worms
  Garlic
  Pumpkin seeds
  Oregon Grape

Wounds (minor)
  Aloe
  Calendula
  Cayenne
  Comfrey
  Oregon Grape
  St. John's Wort

Brown, Donald J., N.D. *Herbal Prescriptions for Better Health: Your Everyday Guide to Prevention, Treatment, and Care.* Prima Publishing, 1996.

Castleman, Michael. The Healing Herbs: *The Ultimate Guide to the Curative Power of Nature's Medicines.* Rodale Press, 1991.

de Bairacli Levy, Juliette. *The Complete Herbal Handbook for Farm and Stable,* Faber & Faber, 1988.

--- ibid. *The Complete Herbal Handbook for the Dog and Cat,* Arco Publishing, 1985.

Hoffmann, David. *The Holistic Herbal.* Element Books, 1988.

Jones, Feather, Clinical Herbalist. *Medicinal Herb Handbook.*

Kindscher, Kelly. *Medicinal Plants of the Prairie, An Ethnobotanical Guide.* University of Kansas Press, 1992

Lazarus, Pat. *Keep Your Pet Healthy the Natural Way,* Keats Publishing, 1986.

Merck Veterinary Manual. Merck and Co., Inc. 1991

Moore, Michael. *Medicinal Plants of the Pacific West.* Red Crane Books,1993.

---ibid. *Herbal/Medical Contraindications.*

Mowrey, Daniel B., Ph.D. *The Scientific Validation of Herbal Medicine.* Keats Publishing, 1986

—ibid. *Herbal Tonic Therapies.* Keats Publishing,1993.

Pitcairn, Richard H., D.V.M., and Pitcairn, Susan H. *Dr. Pitcairn's Complete Guide to Natural Health for Dogs and Cats,* Rodale Press, 1995.

Protocol Journal of Botanical Medicine, volume 1, numbers 1,2.3 & 4.

Stein, Diane. *The Natural Remedy Book for Dogs and Cats.* The Crossing Press, 1994

Volhard, Wendy & Brown, Kerry DVM. *The Holistic Guide for a Healthy Dog,* Howell Book House,1995

Yarnall, Celeste. *Cat Care Naturally,* Tuttle, 1995.